my big Cre

ative Activity book

To Mom

from Katy x

Louise Rupnik

priddy books

big ideas for little people

Contents

Note to parents

This book is full of creative ideas that will help you to make the most of the spare time that you spend with your children. These activities will ease the boredom of a rainy day spent indoors and provide a spark to your child's creativity and imagination – a rewarding experience for you both.

Edited by Simon Mugford
Photography by Richard Brown

This book was made by Roger Priddy, Robert Tainsh, Jo Douglass, Dan Green, Jo Rigg, Lizzie Shapland and Amy Oliver.

We hope you enjoy this book as much as we enjoyed making it.

Copyright © 2004 St. Martin's Press, 175 Fifth Avenue, New York, NY 10010.
Published by
priddy🌕books
A division of Macmillan Publishers Ltd
All rights reserved, including the right of reproduction in whole or in part in any form.

Manufactured in Malaysia

What you need

Supplies for creative activities

Getting started

The activities in this book use things you can find at home, or that can be bought from art supply shops. Some of the most commonly used materials are shown here, but always check the 'You will need' section in each activity before you start.

Chopping board

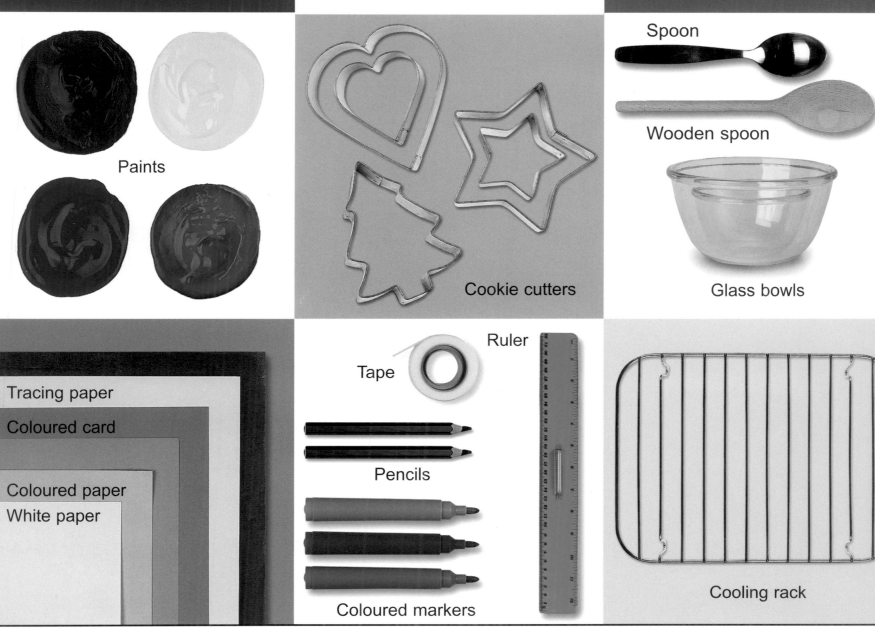

Paints

Cookie cutters

Spoon

Wooden spoon

Glass bowls

Tracing paper

Coloured card

Coloured paper

White paper

Tape

Ruler

Pencils

Coloured markers

Cooling rack

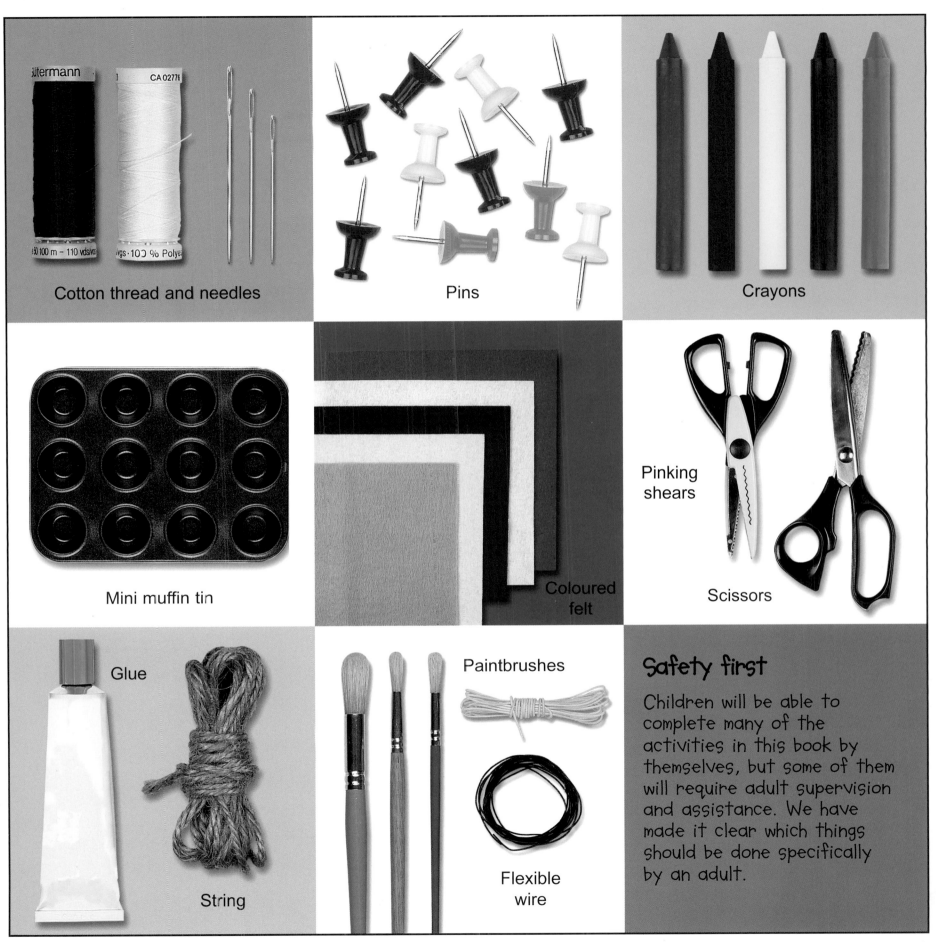

Cotton thread and needles

Pins

Crayons

Mini muffin tin

Coloured felt

Pinking shears

Scissors

Glue

String

Paintbrushes

Flexible wire

Safety first

Children will be able to complete many of the activities in this book by themselves, but some of them will require adult supervision and assistance. We have made it clear which things should be done specifically by an adult.

Animal masks

Creative creature disguises

You will need:

- coloured felt
- card
- scissors ● pencil
- tracing paper
- paintbrush
- elastic ● needle
- glue ● pen
- templates (on pages 11–12)

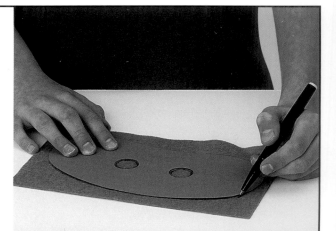

1 Trace the eyepiece template onto card and cut it out. Copy the shape onto a piece of felt.

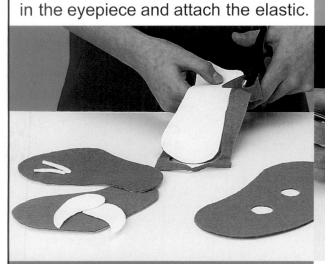

2 Cut a length of elastic to fit around your head. Make holes in the eyepiece and attach the elastic.

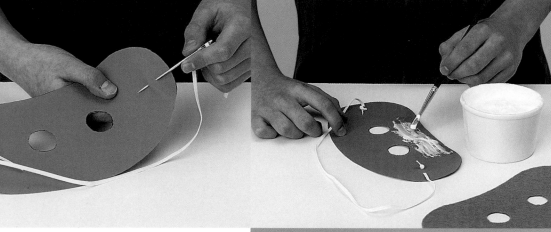

3 Cut out the felt shape and glue it to the card eyepiece.

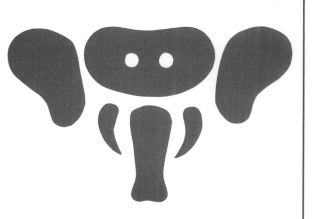

4 Trace the templates of your choice on pages 11 or 12 to make the rest of your chosen mask.

5 Copy the shapes onto felt and cut them out.

6 Glue the felt shapes onto the card pieces.

7 Glue the shapes together to make the masks. Look at the photographs to see how.

Trace over these templates to make the shapes for the masks

Eyepiece (use this shape for all three of the masks)

Trunk

Ears (x2)

Elephant

Tusks (x2)

Cut white strips to add to the trunk

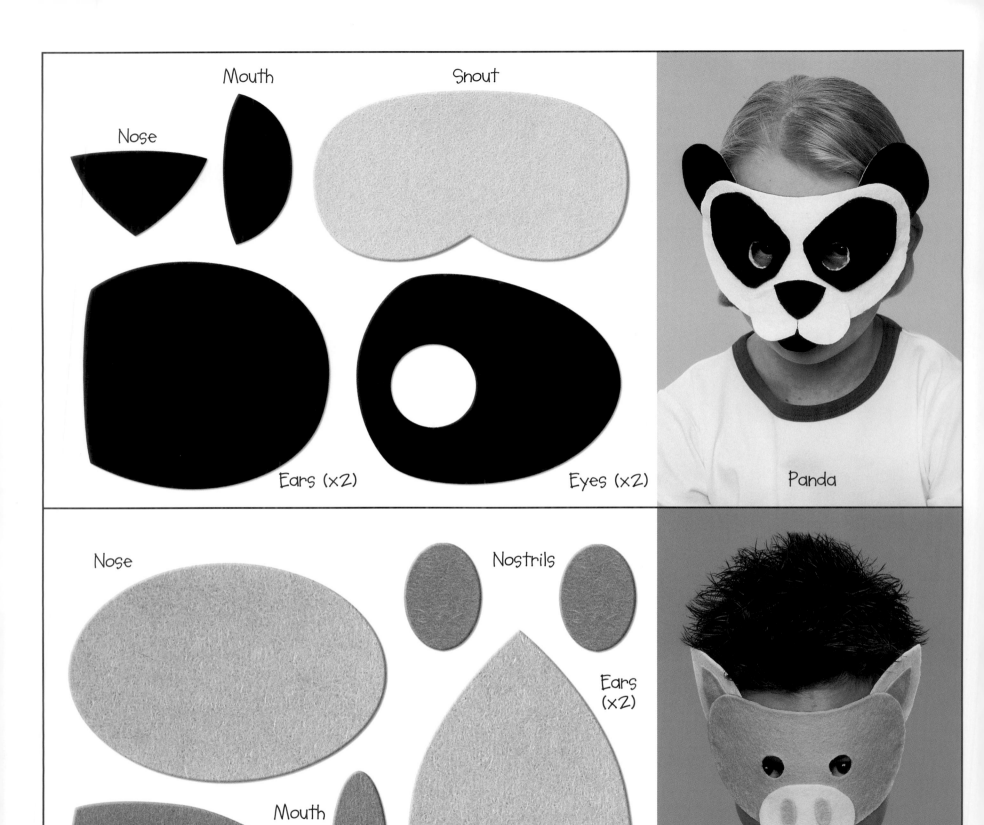

Nose

Mouth

Snout

Ears (x2)

Eyes (x2)

Panda

Nose

Nostrils

Ears (x2)

Mouth

Inner ears (x2)

Pig

Tissue pom-poms

A colourful way to celebrate a special occasion

You will need:

- At least 18 sheets of tissue paper (various colours)
- lollipop sticks
- scissors
- tape

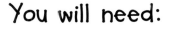

Do not cut all the way

1 Place three sheets of tissue paper together. Fold in half lengthways and cut three-cm wide strips as shown.

2 Starting at one end, roll the folded edge around the end of the lollipop stick.

3 Use tape to secure the pom-pom to the stick. Repeat the process three more times per pom-pom.

4 These pom-poms are perfect for celebrating sports days, birthdays and other special occasions. Of course, they are also perfect for practising to be a cheerleader!

Paper roses

Make some pretty paper flowers

You will need:

- 75 cm × 8 cm piece of yellow crêpe paper
- sheet of green crêpe paper
- flexible wire
- cotton thread
- cotton wool
- pencil • scissors
- glue

1 Cut a 15-cm piece of flexible wire. Add a piece of cotton wool to one end and glue crêpe paper around it.

2 Fold the yellow paper in half crossways, then fold it the same way three more times.

3 Draw a curve around the edge of the paper as shown. Cut around it and unfold the paper.

4 Wrap the petals around the wire and tie cotton thread around the base of the flower.

5 Cut leaf shapes from the green paper. Glue an eight-cm piece of flexible wire between two shapes.

6 Make three to four leaves in this way. Wind the leaf wires around the rose stem.

7 Cover the stem and the leaf wires with a strip of green paper. Glue the end of the paper in place.

These paper roses
make a wonderful
springtime decoration
or Mother's Day gift

Scented pillows

Make a sweet-smelling present

You will need:

- 20 cm x 10 cm piece of white felt
- 8 cm x 8 cm piece of pink felt
- lavender or similar dried, scented flowers
- scissors • ribbon
- sewing needle
- cotton thread
- fabric glue

1 Cut the white felt in half crossways. Cut the pink felt into a heart shape.

2 Sew around the edge of the heart for decoration. Glue it to one of the white squares.

3 Place the two white squares together and sew around three sides, leaving one open.

4 Fill the bag with the lavender. Place a piece of ribbon in one corner to make a loop and secure it in place with fabric glue. Sew up the remaining side of the cushion.

Try different fabrics

The first letter of a name

Pretty flower

This is the design we made

17

Scanner **art**

Use a computer to decorate your stuff

You will need:

- computer
- scanning software
- scanner • colour printer
- coloured paper • ruler
- storage containers
- objects to scan
- paintbrush
- glue • scissors

1 Choose the objects that you wish to scan and the colour of paper you would like to use.

2 Choose a container for the objects. Measure it and make a note of its size.

3 Place the objects on the scanner. Put the paper above them and scan them into your computer.

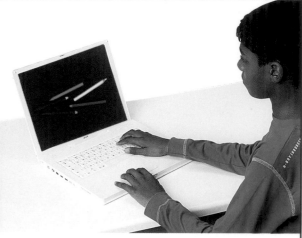

4 Check that the size of the image is big enough to cover the container you are using.

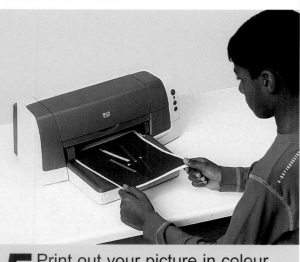

5 Print out your picture in colour. Make sure that you are happy with it.

6 Cut out the picture to the correct size if necessary.

7 Carefully glue the picture to the container. You might need an adult to help you.

Chalk sticks

Coloured pencils

Toy cars

Magnetic numbers

Rainbow crayons

Melt crayons into big rainbow colouring blocks

You will need:
- old coloured crayons
- chopping board
- cooling rack
- kitchen knife
- mini muffin tin

1 Ask an adult to cut the crayons into one-cm long pieces.

2 Preheat an oven to 65°C (cool gas oven). Fill the muffin tin with different-coloured pieces of crayon.

3 Bake for 8 to 9 minutes or until the wax has melted. Allow them to cool and take them out of the tin.

4 If you find that it is difficult to get them out, place them in a freezer for around an hour – they should pop out. You can use your rainbow crayons to quickly produce wonderful multi-coloured pictures.

Friendship tree

Show your friends and family on a tree

You will need:

- as many leaves for all the people you want to include
- glue ● pen
- an old heavy book (such as a telephone directory)
- pieces of paper (for name labels)
- 3 large pieces of brown card
- scissors

1 Collect some pretty coloured leaves. Lay them flat between the pages of a heavy book overnight.

2 Make a card tree with enough branches for your friends and your close family.

3 Make labels for each person you are going to put on your tree and stick one to each leaf.

4 Stick your own leaf at the bottom of the tree, then add all of the other people to the branches. Why not make new branches as you make new friends and your family grows?

Desk organiser

Keep your desk neat and tidy

You will need:

- piece of strong fabric
- pieces of coloured felt
- cotton thread
- sewing needle ● ruler
- scissors ● buttons
- fabric eyelet kit ● iron
- iron-on adhesive tape
- stick-on plastic hooks

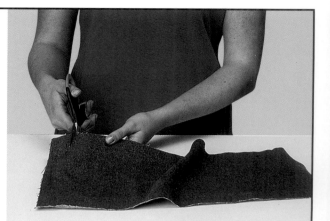

1 Cut out a piece of fabric, 50 cm long by 30 cm wide.

2 Fold in three cm on all four sides. Ask an adult to stick the hems down with the iron-on adhesive tape.

3 Ask an adult to fit an eyelet about three cm in from the corners of the long side.

4 Cut out different coloured pieces of felt to make big pockets. Use pinking shears if you wish.

5 For pockets with flaps, cut out a piece of felt for the pocket and a triangle-shaped piece for the flap.

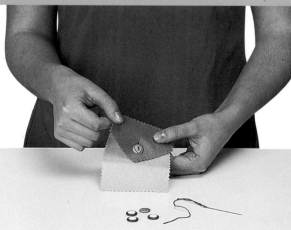

6 Cut a slit in the flap to make a buttonhole. Sew a button onto the pocket.

7 Sew the pockets onto the fabric in the positions that you like.

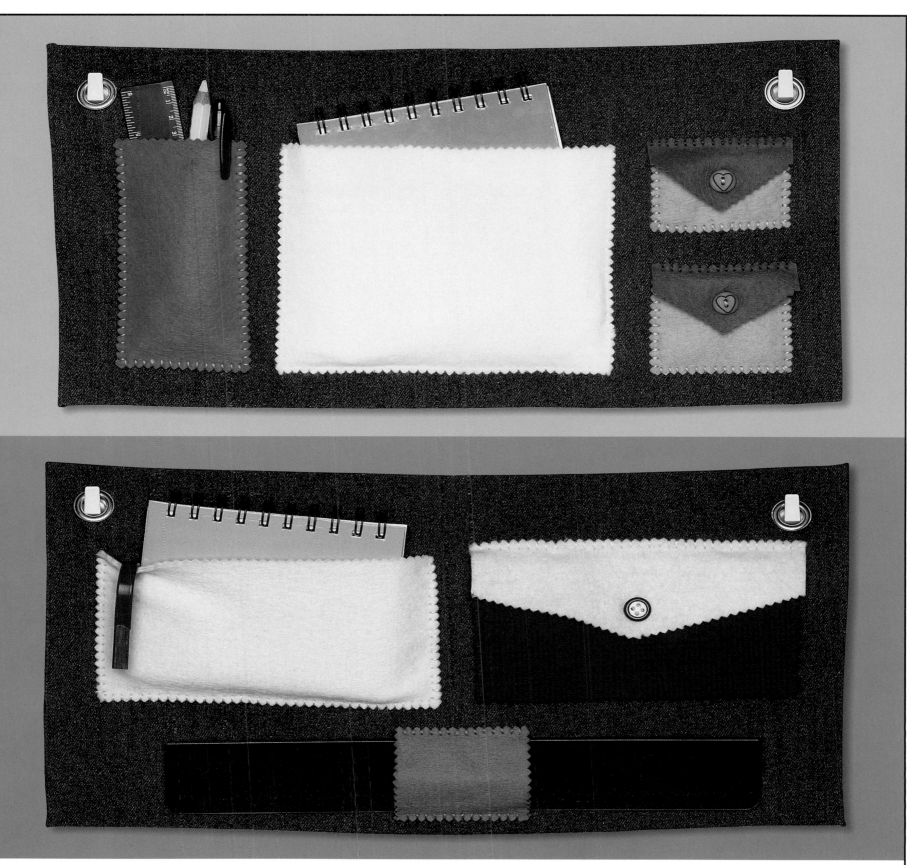

8 Stick two hooks on a wall near your desk the same distance apart as the eyelets. Hang your desk organiser on the hooks and put your stationery in the pockets. Your desk need never be in a mess again!

Book covers

Brighten up your textbooks

You will need:

- books to cover
- coloured or patterned paper – pieces should be 5 cm bigger than the book on all sides
- stickers
- scissors
- glue

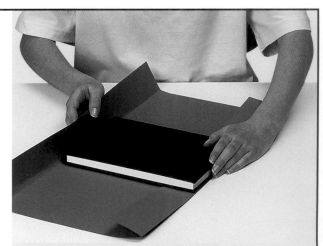

1 Place the book in the centre of the paper. Fold the paper against the top and bottom edges.

2 Place the closed book on the folded paper, five cm from one side. Fold the paper around one cover.

3 Remove the book and fold crisply. Slide the cover into the fold, close and then fold the other side.

4 Fold the creases neatly and slide the other cover into the sleeve. With the book now covered it is ready to decorate. Use some stickers or glue on some pieces of coloured paper.

This is the completed cover with a polka dot design.

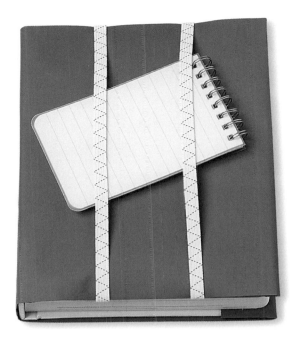

Glue strips of elastic to the inside of the cover and use them to hold a notebook on the outside.

Glue coloured strips to some plain paper, then use it to make a stripy cover.

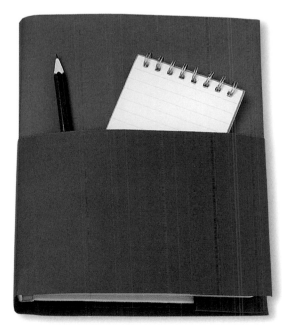

Make a half-size second cover to make a paper sleeve to store notebooks, pens or pencils.

You could try using a piece of fabric as a cover. Use fabric glue to secure the folds inside.

Pictures cut from magazines or picture stickers make good decorations for your covers.

Paper people

Make some colourful card characters

You will need:

- 40 cm x 30 cm sheet of red card
- 2 x 20 cm x 20 cm sheets of green card
- sheets of yellow, brown and orange card
- scissors ● pen
- glue ● tape

Make an orange crown and add green jewels

Add ears

Cut out a two-inch circle from brown card for his head and draw on his features

Make a beard from yellow card

Use yellow and orange card for the coat fasteners

1 To make a Christmas king, roll the red card into a cone. Secure it with a piece of tape.

2 Cut across the large end of the cone to make a base.

3 Glue one green piece of card to the cone. Fold the other piece in half and cut the shape as shown.

4 Glue the shape that you have just cut out to the back of the cone as shown.

Christmas king

Cut a triangle-shaped piece of black card for the hat

White halo

Cut a heart shape for the wings

Hair made from black card

Blue and yellow card headband

The jacket is made from white and yellow card

Magic wand, made from black and white card

Cut yellow card for the stars

Cut strips of red card for the dress

Decorate the wings and gown with yellow strips

Use light blue card for the pattern

Cut a 45° strip of blue card and wrap around the cone to make this pattern

Wizard

Angel

Native American

27

Cupcake creations

Decorate cupcakes for special occasions

You will need:

- ready-made cake mix
- 450 g icing sugar
- 6 tablespoons butter
- sweets for decoration
- food colouring ● mixing bowl
- cupcake liners
- mini cupcake tin
- spoon ● whisk
- cooling rack

1 Mix the cupcake mixture in a bowl according to the instructions on the box.

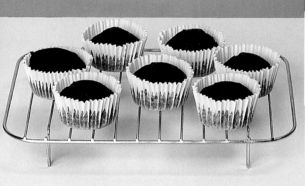

2 Spoon the mixture into the cupcake liners.

3 Bake the cupcakes as directed on the box. Leave them to cool on a cooling rack.

4 Whisk the sugar, butter and a few drops of food colouring together to make the icing.

5 Ice the cakes using a spoon. You could decorate cakes using different colours of icing.

6 Use your favourite sweets to decorate the cupcakes.

7 Try different designs and colours for special occasions – see the opposite page for some ideas.

Snowman — Jelly sweet pieces · Two marshmallows

Valentine heart — Sugar-coated chocolate sweets

Chocolate celebrations — Chocolate stars

Gone fishing — Drinking straw · Dental floss · Jelly sweet fish

Stars and stripes — Jelly sweet stripes

Flower — Lollipop · Jelly sweet leaf

Marshmallow heart — Marshmallow

Baseball — Jelly sweet laces

Holly and berries — Jelly sweet leaves · Sugar-coated chocolates

Friendship **necklaces**

Special jewellery for you and your best friend

1 Thread coloured beads onto a length of elastic a little longer than you need, then tie the ends.

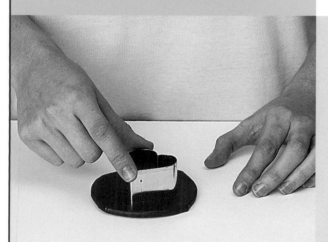

2 Knead a piece of clay until it is soft. Flatten it to a half-cm thick and cut out a heart shape.

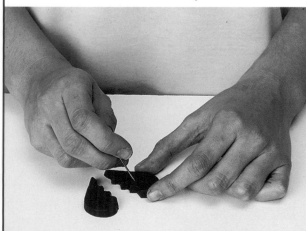

3 Cut the heart with the pinking shears. Write 'Best Friends' across the two halves with a needle.

4 Make small holes in the top of each half of the heart. Bake them for 6-8 minutes in an oven heated to 135°C (cool gas oven) and leave them to cool. Attach the halves to the necklaces using pieces of flexible wire.

Pasta jewellery

Fashion fun with food

You will need:

- thin elastic
- scissors
- beads
- pasta bows
- pasta shapes with holes
- strips of ribbon

1 Cut the lengths of elastic for your bracelets and necklaces a little longer than you actually need.

2 Decide on a design and thread the elastic through the pasta shapes and beads. Tie the ends.

3 Tie strips of ribbon to the pasta bows for extra decoration.

4 We have created two designs as an example of what you can do – why not try some of your own? Pasta jewellery makes a great gift, or you can use it when you are playing dressing up games with your friends!

Valentine heart bag

Make a special gift for Valentine's Day

You will need:

- 20 cm × 7 cm piece of red felt
- 20 cm × 7 cm piece of white felt
- 2 × 7 cm pieces of ribbon
- scissors
- fabric glue

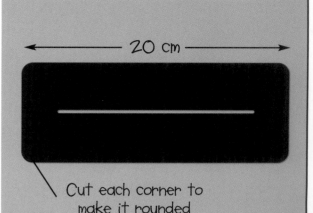

← 20 cm →

Cut each corner to make it rounded

1 Fold the red felt in half crossways and cut a seven-cm slit along the middle (this makes a 14-cm slit).

3 Place the pieces as shown. Note the labels of each strip.

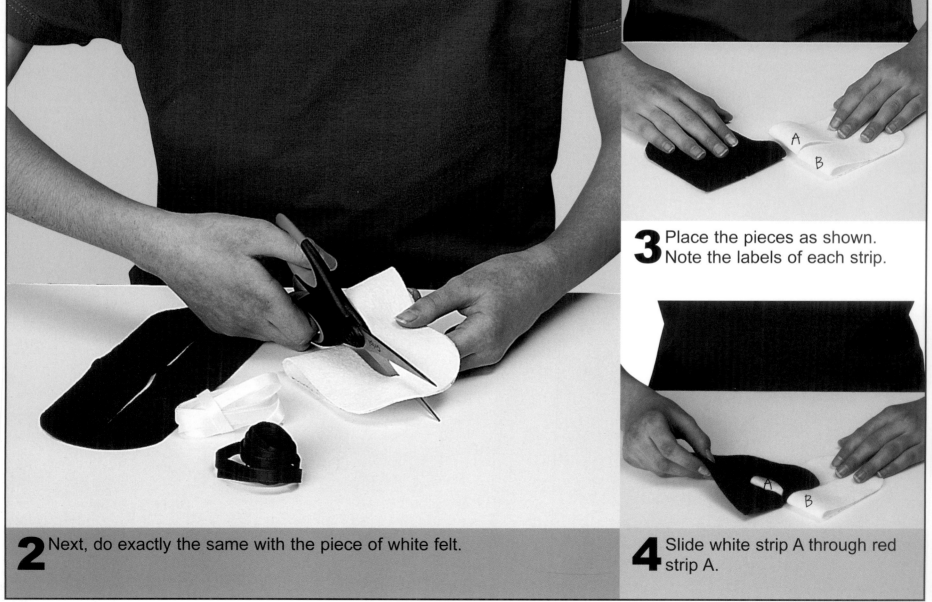

2 Next, do exactly the same with the piece of white felt.

4 Slide white strip A through red strip A.

Lift B and slide into A

5 Pull white strip A until it is on top of red strip B. Then slide red strip B into white strip A.

6 Pull red strips A and B into white strip B.

7 Slide white strip B into red strip B.

8 Finally, glue the two pieces of ribbon to the insides of the heart.

You can fill your Valentine heart with delicious chocolates or pretty flowers

Bird feeders

Attract birds to your garden or balcony

You will need:

- scraps of food, such as breadcrumbs, cheese, cooked rice or vegetables
- birdseed ● lard ● peanuts
- mixing bowl ● saucepan
- plastic cup ● small twig
- large pine cone ● large needle
- scissors ● spoon ● drill
- string ● small log ● hook

1 Mix the scraps with some bird-seed and nuts in a bowl. Ask an adult to melt the lard in a saucepan.

2 Add the melted lard to the mixture and stir it all together with the spoon.

3 Put some of the mixture into the plastic cup and push a twig into the middle. Leave it to set.

4 Pull the mixture out of the cup and roll it in some birdseed. Tie a piece of string to the twig.

5 To make a pine cone feeder, simply push the mixture between the gaps in a pine cone.

6 To make a peanut kebab, use a needle to thread string through peanut shells and balls of mixture.

7 To make a log feeder, ask an adult to drill holes in a small log and fill them with the mixture.

This feeder is made using a gourd. You could use a small pumpkin or a melon

Peanut kebab

Plastic cup feeder

Log feeder

Pine cone feeder

8 Hang out your bird feeders and watch your feathered friends come to feed!

Pebble caterpillar

Make a 10-legged rocky creature

You will need:

- 6 smooth, rounded pebbles
- ice lolly sticks
- strong glue
- acrylic paint
- paintbrush
- 6 pipe cleaners

1 Arrange the pebbles in a zig-zag shape. Glue ice lolly sticks across them and leave to dry.

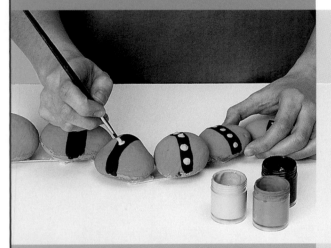

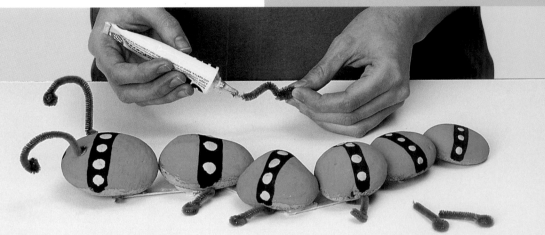

2 Carefully turn the pebbles over and paint on a caterpillar pattern. Leave the paint to dry.

3 Cut and bend the pipe cleaners to make two feelers and five pairs of legs. Glue them to the caterpillar in the positions shown.

You could copy this pattern or create your own design. See the pictures on the opposite page for some more rock painting ideas

Stars and spirals

Hearts and flowers

Bugs and creepy crawlies

Spots and stripes

37

Mini desert

Create your own desert garden

You will need:

- succulents (plants with fleshy leaves and stems that store water, such as cacti)
- container (about 8 cm deep)
- gravel ● compost
- decorative stones
- watering can ● trowel

1 Half-fill the container, first with a thin layer of gravel, then with a layer of compost.

2 Decide how you want to arrange the plants before you take them out of their pots.

3 Remove the plants from their pots and plant them in compost. Place decorative stones around them.

4 Water the plants lightly when you have finished. Place your mini desert in a sunny window. These plants like to dry out and then be well watered, so check that they are dry before you water them.

Flowering Cacti

Jade Plant

Agave

Flaming Katy

Sedum

Herb garden

Grow a pot full of flavours for the kitchen

You will need:

- small herb plants, such as parsley, chives, purple sage, thyme and basil
- trowel ● watering can
- compost ● gravel
- large container

1 Put a layer of gravel about five cm deep in the bottom of the container.

2 Add compost until the container is about three-quarters full.

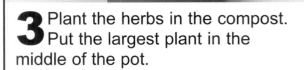

3 Plant the herbs in the compost. Put the largest plant in the middle of the pot.

4 Push the compost down firmly around the plants, adding more if needed. Water the herbs well. Trimming or picking the herbs regularly will help them to grow and keep their flavour.

Thyme

Basil

Purple Sage

Lemon
Thyme

Chives

Chives

Parsley

Marbled eggs

Decorate eggs for a colourful Easter

You will need:

- hard boiled eggs
- bowl or saucepan
- crayons
- cheese grater
- plate
- hot water
- thick cardboard
- tacks or pins
- spoon

1 Push tacks or pins through a piece of cardboard as shown. This is a stand for drying the eggs.

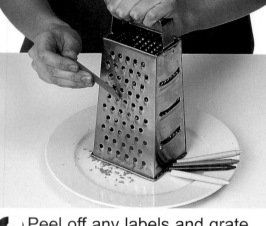

2 Peel off any labels and grate the crayons up into fine pieces.

3 Ask an adult to fill a bowl with very hot water. Add the grated crayon pieces.

4 Dip an egg fully into the water using a spoon. Cover it in as much wax as you can.

5 Remove the egg slowly up through the wax. Place it on the stand and leave the wax to set.

6 Decorate as many eggs as you can in the same way using different colours of crayon. Try using mixtures of colours to get a really crazy rainbow effect.

A basket full of brightly coloured eggs makes an excellent Easter decoration

Pressed flowers

Decorative ideas with pressed petals

You will need:

- freshly-picked flowers
- blotting paper
- several large, heavy books
- paintbrush
- white card
- holepunch
- ribbon
- glue
- scissors

1 Collect some flowers and leaves. Choose a varied selection of colours and types.

2 Fold the blotting paper in half crossways. Open it up and place it in the centre of the book.

3 Arrange the flowers flat on one side of the blotting paper. Leave plenty of space between them.

4 Carefully fold the paper, then close the book. Place more heavy books on top of it and leave the flowers to press flat and dry out. This should take about three to four weeks.

5 After that time, carefully open the blotting paper and remove the dried, pressed flowers.

6 To make gift tags, cut out pieces of card on which to mount the flowers.

7 Fold the card and glue the flowers on one side. Punch a hole in the corner and add the ribbon.

You could also make pretty bookmarks like these or why not try some birthday cards?

Easter pictures

How to draw pictures for Easter

1 For a spring flower, draw the petals in the top-right of your piece of paper.

2 Add the stem and leaves as shown. Use your favourite colour for the petals.

1 To draw an Easter bunny, start with two egg shapes for the body and head.

2 Add the outlines of the ears, fluffy tail and feet.

3 Finally, add the details of the eyes, whiskers and toes. Finish by colouring in your bunny.

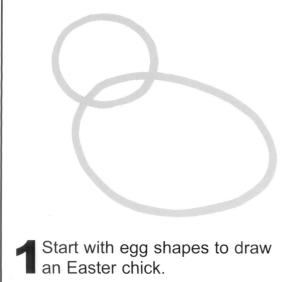

1 Start with egg shapes to draw an Easter chick.

2 Add the outlines of the beak, wings and feet.

3 Finish by adding eyes and detail to the beak, wings and feet. Give the chick a fluffy look and colour it in.

Spooky sweets

Chocolate ghosts on sticks for Halloween

You will need:

- 340 g white chocolate
- milk chocolate drops
- 1½ tablespoons vegetable oil
- heatproof bowl ● saucepan
- lollipop sticks
- teaspoon
- tablespoon
- baking tray
- greaseproof paper

1 Ask an adult to melt the white chocolate in a bowl, over a pan of hot water. Then add the vegetable oil.

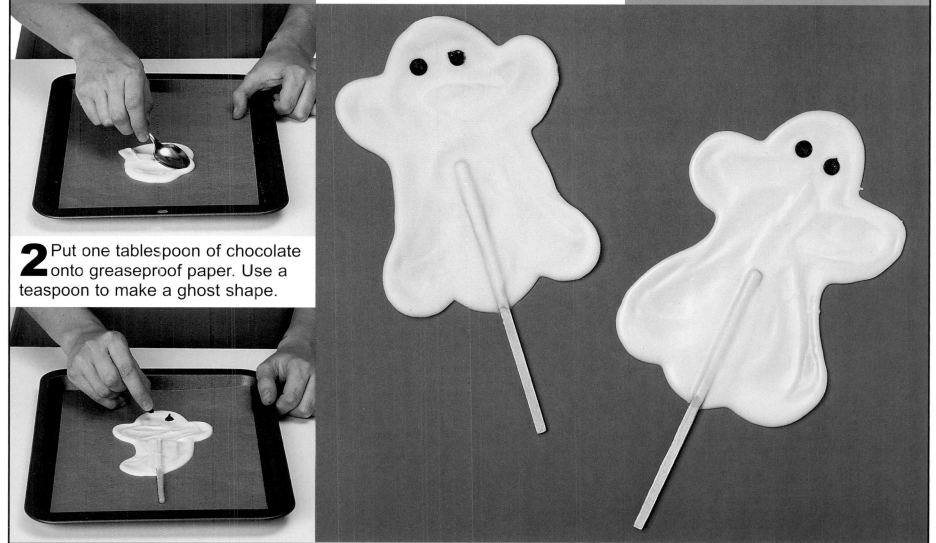

2 Put one tablespoon of chocolate onto greaseproof paper. Use a teaspoon to make a ghost shape.

3 Add two chocolate drops for ghostly eyes. Press a lollipop stick into the ghost as shown.

4 You should be able to make about 12-15 ghosts with this mixture. Leave them to cool in the refrigerator for about 5 minutes, then carefully peel them off the paper. Try some creepy designs of your own!

Halloween pumpkins

Learn how to light up your house at Halloween

You will need:

- pumpkins
- metal spoon
- sharp knife ● tape
- bowl ● pen ● paper
- chopping board
- pins or toothpicks
- candles and holders
- apple corer

1 Draw a face onto a pumpkin. You could copy the one shown on these pages.

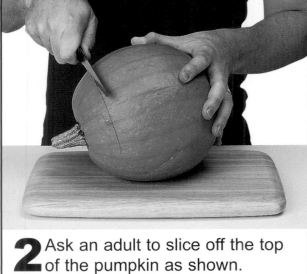

2 Ask an adult to slice off the top of the pumpkin as shown.

3 Scoop out the insides of the pumpkin with a spoon.

4 Carefully cut out the detail with a knife. Ask an adult to help you if necessary.

1 An alternative method is to draw your design on paper and stick it to the pumpkin.

2 Press through the outline using a pin or a toothpick to make small holes in the pumpkin.

3 Then use a knife to fully cut out the shape. You can use this method for complicated shapes.

Whichever design you choose, to finish your Halloween pumpkin, put a candle in a holder and put it inside the pumpkin. Ask an adult to light it. For smaller pumpkins, you could use tea lights instead of candles. Put your pumpkin on display where it will spook your friends and neighbours!

Pumpkin lanterns

More creative ideas for your pumpkins

You could try using a melon

Use an apple corer to make these holes

This moon and stars design is ideal for Halloween

1 Use a template to mark your design onto the pumpkin as on the previous page.

2 Make shallow cuts into the pumpkin's skin and scrape away to complete the pattern.

3 You could carve your house number into a pumpkin to hang outside your house. Experiment with designs of your own. You could try using other fruit and vegetables.

Why not try to make this seasonally spooky Halloween owl? The pumpkins are held together with toothpicks

Stick leaves to the top of the head

Pumpkin seeds are glued to a piece of card and pinned in place

Hazelnuts make the eyes

The legs are made using twigs

Use long, thin leaves to make the wings

Halloween **pictures**

Some spooky things to copy for Halloween

1 Start drawing a ghost by copying the squiggly shape above.

2 Finish by adding its tail and a spooky expression on its face.

1 Start drawing a beastly bat with these two shapes that make its body.

2 Add wings and some pointed bat ears.

3 Add details to the wings and face. Then draw on the feet.

1 Draw an egg shape for a witch's face. Draw the outline of her crooked hat as shown.

2 Add her hair and a big, ugly nose.

3 Add some detail to her hat and finish with a really mean-looking face.

Christmas pictures

Copy or trace these seasonal drawings

1 For some holly and berries, start by drawing three small circles together.

2 Add the holly leaves as above and colour in the berries.

1 To draw Rudolph the Red-nosed Reindeer, start with a slightly squashed egg shape.

2 Add the outlines of Rudolph's nose and ears.

3 Now draw the eyes, antlers and finish the ears. Don't forget to colour his nose red!

1 Santa Claus has a big, round friendly face.

2 Next, draw his nose and the outline of his bobble hat.

3 Finally, draw his eyes, mouth and finish the hat. Give his beard and bobble a furry outline.

53

Pom-pom **wreath**

A seasonal snowball decoration

You will need:

- 25 cm diameter circle of thick cardboard
- 24 5 cm cotton balls
- 15 2 cm cotton balls
- holly, or similar seasonal decorations
- glue • ruler • scissors
- pencil • pair of compasses
- paintbrush • ribbon

1 Draw a 20-cm diameter circle on the cardboard. Cut it out with a pair of scissors.

2 Glue the large cotton balls onto the cardboard first, then stick the smaller ones in between.

3 Glue the decorations in place between the cotton balls. Leave the glue to set for two hours.

Hang your wreath with a piece of ribbon

Potato print **gift wrap**

Design your own wrapping paper

You will need:

- large potato
- knife
- paint
- paper
- blank gift tags
- chopping board
- ribbon

1 Ask an adult to cut a potato in half lengthways

2 Ask your adult helper to cut out the shape of a Christmas tree in one half of the potato.

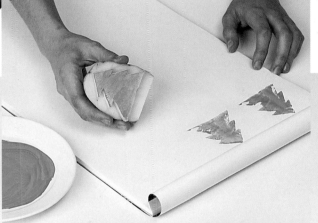

3 Press the tree shape into some green paint. Practise printing the shapes on some paper.

4 Cut a shape for the Christmas tree pot in the other half of the potato.

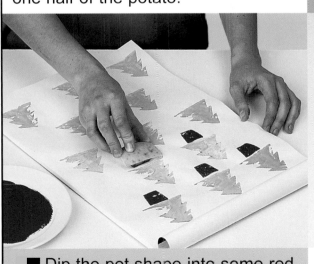

5 Dip the pot shape into some red paint. Use it to complete your Christmas tree design.

6 Print your design onto some gift tags. Leave the paint to dry before writing on them!

Now you can wrap presents with your own design

55

Cookie stars

Shiny Christmas decorations that you can eat

You will need:

- ready-made cookie dough mixture
- selection of clear boiled sweets
- greaseproof paper
- non-stick baking tray
- drinking straw • star-shaped cookie cutters (2 sizes)
- rolling pin • spatula
- coloured string • cooling rack

1 Make up the cookie dough according to the instructions on the box and roll it out flat.

2 Cut out stars with the largest cookie cutter. Make another star inside with the smaller cutter.

3 Chop the sweets into small pieces and place them in the centre of the cookies.

4 Use a drinking straw to make a small hole in the top of each cookie. Bake in an oven pre-heated to the temperature shown in the cookie mixture instructions. Do not let the sweets start to bubble.

5 Remove the cookies from the oven and allow them to cool thoroughly on a cooling rack. When they are cool, thread some coloured string through the holes and tie them off. Now your cookies are ready to be hung on a Christmas tree – how long will you be able to resist eating them all?

Sweet **tree**

Decorate a Christmas tree with treats

You will need:

- Christmas tree
- selection of colourful sweets
- flexible wire
- thin elastic
- sewing needle
- scissors

1 Gather together a selection of your favourite sweets. Jelly types are the easiest to use.

2 To make a sweet jewel decoration, take two different jelly sweets.

3 Cut a seven-cm piece of flexible wire. Bend it at one end and push it through a sweet.

4 Push the other sweet onto the wire. Bend the top of the wire to make a hook.

1 To make a jelly bean chain, first thread a length of elastic onto a sewing needle.

2 Thread jelly beans onto the elastic. Vary the order of the colours as you put them on.

3 When you have filled the elastic, tie the ends to make them secure.

Hang the decorations on your tree and you have some sweet Christmas treats to eat!

Jelly bean chain

Sweet jewel

Coconut sweet

Celebration cookies

Decorate some sweet festive treats

You will need:

- ready-made cookie mixture
- cookie cutters ● spoon
- rolling pin ● greaseproof paper
- non-stick baking tray
- piping bag and attachments
- ready-made royal icing mixture
- palette knife ● sanding sugar
- food colouring ● mixing bowl
- cooling rack ● cake decorations

1 Make up the cookie dough according to the instructions on the box and roll it out flat.

2 Use cookie cutters to make shapes, or you could try cutting your own shapes.

3 Place them on greaseproof paper, on a baking tray. Bake them according to the mixture instructions.

4 Carefully remove them from the tray and leave them to cool on a cooling rack.

5 Make the royal icing according to the instructions on the box. Add your choice of food colouring.

6 Use the piping bag to draw an outline of icing. Leave it to set, then fill the outline with more icing.

7 Use a palette knife to spread the icing. Add any other decorations to the soft icing.

60

Holly leaf

Christmas tree

Love heart

Stars

Snow flakes

Bring a white Christmas indoors

You will need:

- white paper
- blue paper
- shiny paper
- tracing paper
- scissors
- ribbon
- cotton thread
- glitter
- glue

1 Cut out a 15-cm square piece of paper.

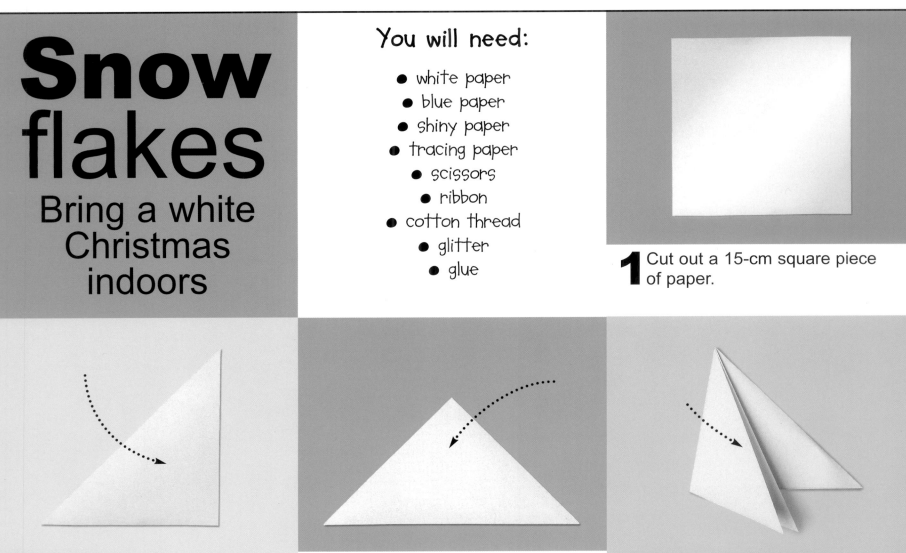

2 Fold the square in half diagonally. You should have a triangle like the one above.

3 Fold the triangle in half so that the corners meet, as above.

4 Now you need to fold the triangle into thirds. First, fold it from left to right.

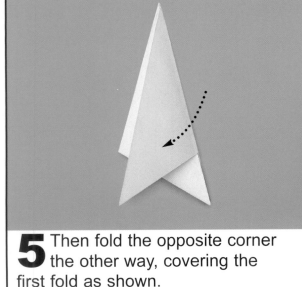

5 Then fold the opposite corner the other way, covering the first fold as shown.

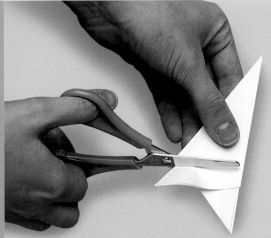

6 Cut straight across the bottom of the triangle.

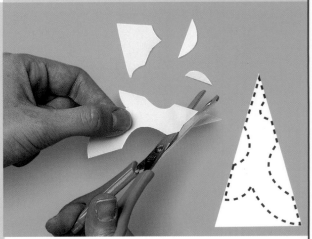

7 Carefully cut out a design. Follow the template shown here to start.

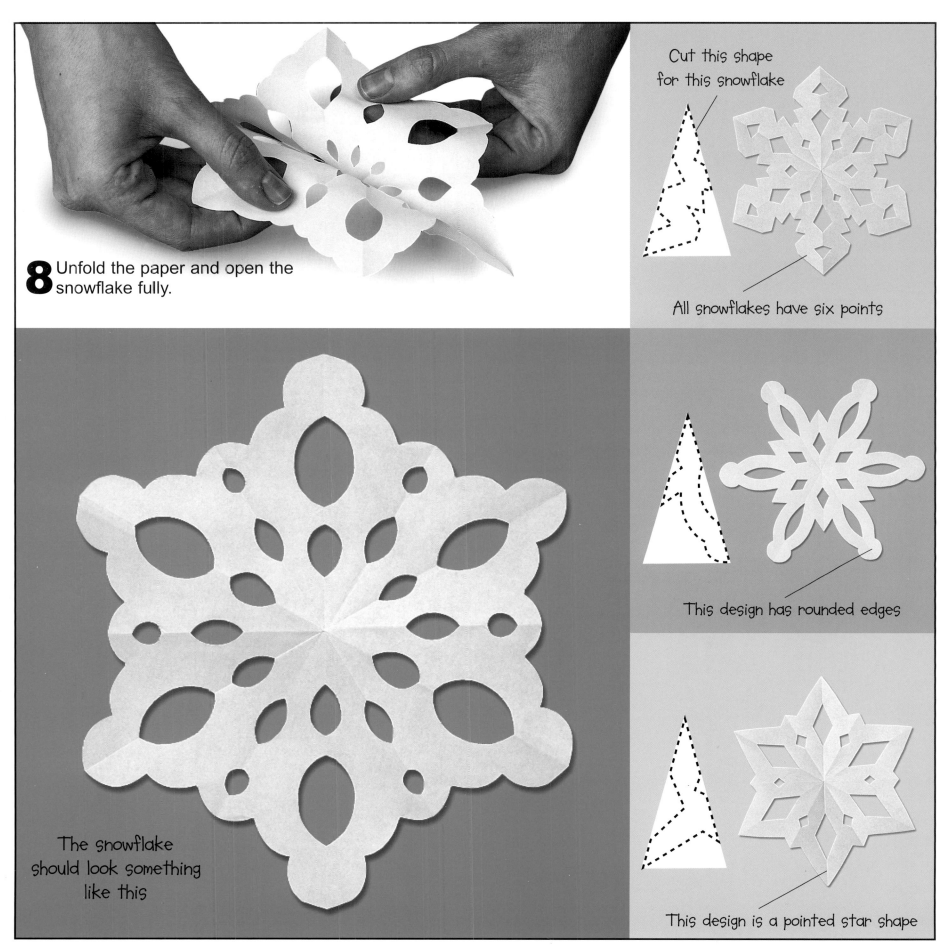

8 Unfold the paper and open the snowflake fully.

Cut this shape for this snowflake

All snowflakes have six points

The snowflake should look something like this

This design has rounded edges

This design is a pointed star shape

Snow flakes

Creative uses for your snowflake designs

Shiny paper

How many different snowflakes can you make?

Tracing paper

Use them to decorate Christmas gifts

To Mom

from Katy x

Hang them on ribbon to make a festive snowflake chain

Hang them on thread to make a mobile

These are made from blue paper and decorated with glitter

Jam jar lantern

Make a colourful glowing lantern

You will need:

- jam jar
- glass paint
- glass outliner paste
- paintbrush
- flexible wire
- tea light
- paper
- pencil

1 Clean the jam jar thoroughly. Draw your design onto a piece of paper and place it inside the jar.

2 Use the outliner paste to copy the design onto the glass. Leave to dry for 24 hours.

3 Paint around your design with the glass paint. Leave to dry for 48 hours.

4 Tightly wrap a length of flexible wire around the rim of the jar.

5 Make a loop by attaching another length of wire to the wire around the rim.

6 Place a tea light in the jar and ask an adult to light it. All you need is somewhere to hang it!

Index

Other Titles in the Series

My Picture Atlas

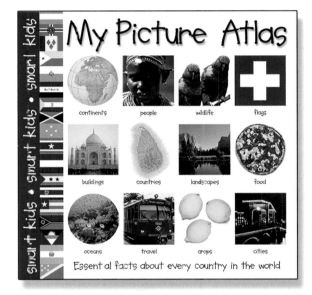

1-84332-127-0

£12.99

My Big Science Book

1-84332-134-3

£9.99

My Fun Picture Dictionary

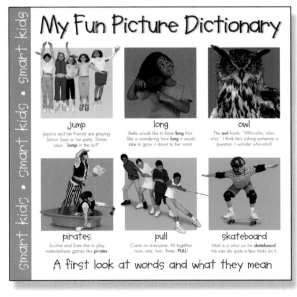

1-84332-076-2

£9.99

My Big Word Book

1-84332-055-X

£9.99